A GUIDE TO THE

ORTHODOX JEWISH

WAY OF LIFE

FOR

HEALTHCARE PROFESSIONALS

By

DR JOSEPH SPITZER
MB BS FRCGP DCCH DRCOG

GW00580194

Third Revised Edition
Revised and Expanded

Third revised edition
© Dr J Spitzer 2005
ISBN 0 9532343 1 2

All rights reserved. No part of this publication may be reproduced, copied or stored in a retrieval system, or transmitted, in any form or by any means without prior written permission.

Published by
Dr J Spitzer
The Surgery, 62 Cranwich Road,
London N16 5JF

Telephone: (020) 8802 2002 Fax: (020) 8880 2112
E-mail: j.spitzer@doctors.org.uk

First edition 1996
Dr J Spitzer & Ms N Vyras 1996
Published jointly by
The Department of General Practice and Primary Care
St Bartholomew's and the Royal London School of Medicine and Dentistry
and the
East London and The City Health Authority

Second edition 1998, Third Edition 2002 & 2005
Published by Dr J Spitzer

Printed by
Senprint
Rear of 16 Russell Parade
Golders Green Road
London NW11 9NN
(020) 8731 8797

By the same author
"Caring for Jewish Patients"
Radcliffe Medical Press
ISBN 1 85775 991 5

CONTENTS

PREFACE

This booklet was conceived when my practice nurse, Nicky Vyras was preparing for the Health Education Certificate at The College of North East London. As part of her course work she produced a short pamphlet giving brief information on the Orthodox Jewish way of life for her peers. She felt that as she works so closely with the Jewish community, it would be appropriate to share her experience and produce a booklet for other health professionals also working with this community, giving useful information about certain aspects of the Orthodox Jewish life.

I felt that instead of being left to gather dust, the work should be rewritten, expanded and circulated, as its contents would be of value to other healthcare professionals working within the Orthodox Jewish community.

Ms Vyras (who is not Jewish) and I work together in a general practice in the Stamford Hill area of North Hackney in North London. The practice is located in the heart of a large Orthodox Jewish (mainly Hassidic) community and a high proportion of our patients is drawn from this community. Both the doctors in the practice are Orthodox Jews.

The Hassidic Jewish community choose to lead an insular existence and not many avenues are open to enable one to explore their rich culture. Ms Vyras felt that having worked within this community and having established a relationship of trust with many patients over the years she was in an ideal position to gain information and insight. In her original course work she was closely advised and guided by me and the first edition of this booklet was a joint reworking and expansion of the original very concise text.

We presented the first edition of this booklet to colleagues in an effort to inform them about the Orthodox Jewish community and thereby to increase understanding and awareness of this group.

Third Edition (2002 - reprinted in 2005 with minor changes)

The first two editions of this booklet published in 1996 and 1998 respectively were very well received. Copies were distributed to healthcare professionals not just in our area but elsewhere in the UK in areas with Orthodox Jewish patients. The text has formed the basis for several other publications by various authors and organisations who (with permission) have adapted it to their own requirements.

I thank colleagues who read draft versions of this and the previous editions for their helpful suggestions, many of which have been included in the text. Comments from readers have not only been very positive but also encouragingly constructive. I have taken the opportunity to incorporate many of these suggestions into this revised and expanded third edition and I would again welcome readers' constructive comments.

Joseph Spitzer MB BS FRCGP DCCH DRCOG
General Practitioner and Honorary Senior Clinical Lecturer in General Practice and Primary Care (Barts and the London, Queen Mary's School of Medicine and Dentistry, University of London)

The Surgery, 62 Cranwich Road
London N16 5JF

Tel: (020) 8802 2002   Fax: (020) 8880 2112
Email: j.spitzer@doctors.org.uk

Readers interested in a more detailed treatment of this subject are referred to my book "CARING FOR JEWISH PATIENTS" (Radcliffe Medical Press [www.radcliffe-oxford.com]) 2003 - ISBN 1 85775 991 5)

CHAPTER 1

INTRODUCTION AND BACKGROUND

What is Judaism?

Judaism is a monotheistic religion, the single most important principle of which is a belief that everything in the universe is under the direct control of the one God. All aspects of Judaism, whether relating to belief, philosophy, religious or civil law, have their basis in the *Torah,* "The Written Law" (the Bible or Old Testament) as interpreted by the Rabbis throughout the ages in "The Oral Law". The main repository of the Oral law is the *Talmud,* a vast (3rd - 6th century) encyclopaedic work covering all aspects of Judaism and Jewish law. The Talmud and its many commentaries are regularly studied in great depth by Orthodox Jewish men and it forms the basis of religious authority in Orthodox Judaism. Almost all subsequent Jewish legal works are based on the Talmud, which remains the cornerstone of Jewish law to this very day. Both the Written and Oral Laws are seen as being inseparable and are taken as being one unit, together often also collectively referred to as the *Torah.* The actual practice of Judaism requires observance of the *mitzvos* – the commandments, the religious obligations incumbent on all Jews.

Who is a Jew?

According to Jewish law a person is Jewish if his or her mother is Jewish. One is born a Jew and remains so all one's life. Judaism is not a religion that seeks to convince or convert the rest

7

of mankind to its own views and there is no missionary element to Judaism. Jews regard Judaism as being for those born as Jews, indeed those who seek conversion are positively discouraged. Under rare circumstances it may be possible to convert to Judaism through a recognised Rabbinical Authority *(Beis Din)*, following which the convert *(ger)* becomes a full Jew in all respects and is required to observe all the commandments *(mitzvos)*; a sincere convert is held in high esteem. Conversion is regarded as being an irreversible process and children born to a woman who has converted are also Jewish.

Having been born a Jew one is regarded in Jewish law as being a full Jew. There are Jews all around the world and there is considerable variation amongst Jews themselves – e.g. there are European and Oriental Jews, there are white and black Jews, there are American and British Jews. There are Jews whose entire 'Jewishness' goes no further than their merely having been born of a Jewish mother. (While these may not regard themselves as being Jewish, Jewish law nevertheless regards them as full Jews). At the other extreme, there are those Jews (including the Orthodox and the *Hassidim*) whose entire way of life is inseparable from their being Jewish. They adhere strictly to Jewish law, conducting their lives according to the dictates of the *Torah*; they regard themselves as being the only truly authentic Jews. Of course, in between these two extremes there is a wide spectrum of Jews of all types.

Practices that are acceptable to one group of Jews may be anathemous to others and healthcare workers must be cautious in extrapolating what they see in their non-Orthodox and less strictly observant patients to their Orthodox ones. For instance, ward staff in hospital may become confused when for example, one Jewish patient would be quite happy to accept a cup of tea, served in hospital crockery containing non-supervised milk, whereas another Jewish patient would vehemently refuse to do so, insisting on drinking only from a disposable plastic cup or one brought in from home and using only supervised kosher milk.

World Jewry

Modern world Jewry can be divided into two main subgroups, the *Ashkenazim* and the *Sefardim*. In broad terms, *Sefardim* include Jews whose origins were in North Africa, Southern Europe, the Levant, the Middle East and the Orient. The Jews who were expelled from Spain in 1492 were *Sefardim* and of these, some settled in Holland, accounting for the small number of *Sefardim* of North European descent. *Ashkenazim* originate from Northern, Central and Eastern Europe. Culturally, *Sefardim* are much more diverse than *Ashkenazim*, for instance, Jews of Yemen have very different customs and practices to those originating from Morocco. *Ashkenazim* subdivide into two main groups, *Hassidim* and *Misnagdim* ('the opponents' i.e. those *Ashkenazi* Jews who are not *Hassidim* and who do not share all their philosophical views). However, since the major upheavals of the Second World War distinctions between the various groups, especially amongst the *Ashkenazim* have started to blur.

Hassidim

The title *Hassid* (the 'H' is pronounced with a hard '*ch*' as in the Scottish lo*ch*, the word can be transliterated either as *Hassid* as used in this booklet, or as *Chassid*) plural *Hassidim*, literally means 'The Righteous (or Pious) One(s)'. The Hassidic movement was started in 17th century Poland by the followers of the famous Rabbi, the *Ba'al Shem Tov* (the 'Master of the Good

Name') and was spread rapidly throughout Eastern Europe by his disciples. The movement split into many branches each led by its own rabbi, known to Hassidim as a *'Rebbe'*, the leadership being passed down, often in dynastic fashion, over many generations. Many Hassidim lived in rural environments, leading a secluded way of life, insulated from the influences of the gentile world outside.

Following the destruction of their traditional way of life in the Holocaust, the remnants of the Hassidic movement settled in several centres around the world, particularly in New York, Israel, Belgium and London, where they slowly began to recreate their traditional way of life, regrouping themselves around their various *Rebbes*.

The Orthodox Tradition

Strictly observant Jews have been termed 'orthodox' (or even 'ultra–orthodox') Jews. This booklet relates to this 'Orthodox Jewish community'. The best known and most conspicuous subgroup of Orthodox Jews are the *Hassidim* (or Hassidic Jews), a large community of whom live in North-east London. Apart from the *Hassidim*, there are sizeable communities of Orthodox *Misnagdim* and *Sefardim*. There are certain differences in practice between 'Hassidic' and other 'Orthodox' Jews and these have been highlighted where appropriate.

Orthodox Jews do not regard Judaism as just a 'religion', but more as a way of life. They do not compartmentalise their lives into religious and secular portions and times. To them, Judaism is an all encompassing way of life based on the *Torah*. However, they do live in the secular world, thereby coming into daily contact with the non-Jewish society around them. In this country, the major portion of their healthcare needs are provided through the National Health Service, thus they come into contact with healthcare workers, many of whom will not have had any previous insight into the Orthodox Jewish way of life.

An example of an area where an understanding of the Orthodox Jewish way of life is of relevance to healthcare workers is in the presentation of conditions such as early dementia, confusion and many psychiatric conditions. Here the patient's aberrant behaviour may be manifested in inappropriate religious or ritual practices which might only be apparent to someone who fully understands the patients religious, social and cultural background. For instance, whereas praying several times a day is part of the normal daily ritual of the Orthodox Jewish male, saying the special *Shabbos* prayers on any other day of the week should give rise to concerns about that persons state of mind. Similarly a Jewish housewife who lights her *Shabbos* candles at any time other than on a Friday evening, would raise similar concerns.

This booklet aims to provide healthcare workers with some background information and insight into this particular community, whose way of life is so very different to the society around them within which they live.

British Jewry

History & Background

There is evidence that Jews first settled in the British Isles during the Roman occupation, where they continued to live until they were expelled in 1290 during the reign of Edward the First. Following their re-admission to England by Oliver Cromwell in the seventeenth century (1656), the first settlers were mainly Dutch merchants. The main influx of Jews into London occurred during the latter part of the nineteenth century when large numbers arrived from Eastern Europe, having fled the pogroms, anti-Semitism and poverty. These immigrants were mainly impoverished craftsmen who settled close to their point of arrival, near the docks in London's East End. Although London had the largest Jewish community at this time, smaller communities were being established throughout the British Isles, mainly in sea ports and industrial towns.

London's Jewish population was at the turn of the twentieth century centred around the East End, which was heavily populated with a poor but industrious community. As their situation improved they gradually moved out of the East End to the then fashionable Hackney, Stamford Hill and Clapton areas. The next wave of movement was further north and east to London's new suburbs. During the thirties and after the Second World War there was a further influx of European Jews, many of whom settled in the Hackney area. In the post-war years these groups have been added to by the arrival of some *Sefardi* groups, mainly from India, North Africa, Iran and Yemen. However, in the last twenty five years or so the main growth in the Stamford Hill area of Hackney has been that of the Hassidic community. Although of Central and Eastern Europe parentage, most are now second or even third generation British by birth.

Beside London, Jewish communities are to be found in many provincial towns and cities in the UK, but most of these are not as Orthodox, as the strictly Orthodox communities now confined to just a few centres.

Apart from the Hackney area, there is also a large Orthodox Jewish community in North-west London (mainly centred around the Golders Green and Hendon areas) but the proportion of these who are traditional Hassidim is much lower than in Stamford Hill. Manchester too has a significant Orthodox Jewish community with a growing proportion of Hassidim. There is a small but strictly Orthodox community in Gateshead in North-east England, of which only a small minority are Hassidic. Most of the other provincial communities have shrunk in recent years and in those that are still viable, the Orthodox element is in the minority.

Hassidic communities are generally very insular, keep themselves to themselves and try to be internally self sufficient. Understandably they may occasionally give the impression of resenting intervention from outside agencies. Healthcare workers such as health visitors or district nurses should bear this in mind when calling on Orthodox Jewish or Hassidic families and they should therefore be careful to explain their roles clearly.

Stamford Hill

The Orthodox Jewish population of North-east London consists of several thousand families who live in the Stamford Hill area of Hackney and the South Tottenham area of Haringey, all within a mile of the main Stamford Hill road junction. The majority are Hassidim and the Hassidic community is itself made up of a number of different groups of various sizes, each with their own synagogues, schools and colleges. The largest and best known groups are Satmar and Lubavitch, both of which are international organisations with their headquarters in New York. Other well known groups include Gur and Belz, also international organisations with their headquarters in Israel.

There are also many non-Hassidic Orthodox Jews living in the same area consisting of both *Ashkenazim* and *Sefardim*. In Stamford Hill the non-Hassidic Orthodox *Ashkenazi* groups consist of *Misnagdim* who make up a reducing proportion of the local Orthodox population. The growing *Sefardi* groups originate mainly from India, North Africa, Iran and Yemen.

North-west London

The Orthodox Jewish community of North-west London which is based around the Golders Green and Hendon areas was founded when some families moved away from the Stamford Hill area in the 1930s and expanded with the arrival of refugees from Europe before and after the Second World War. This is a large, growing Orthodox community of which Hassidim form a smaller proportion then they do in Stamford Hill, with *Misnagdim* making up the majority. In general, the Hassidic groups of North-west London are less insular and more outgoing than their Stamford Hill counterparts. There is also a significant and growing Orthodox *Sefardi* community in North-west London.

Manchester and Gateshead

The Orthodox Jewish and Hassidic communities in Manchester are centred around the Broughton Park and Prestwich areas and are a vibrant and growing centre of traditional authentic Judaism. There are now a number of well established Hassidic groups, each with their own synagogues. There are also a growing number of schools, *yeshivas* (for young men) and seminaries (providing further education) for girls. In recent years, there has been some movement of young couples away from London to Manchester. The Gateshead community is confined to a small area based around the *Yeshiva* and other educational institutions, for which this relatively small but intensely devout community is renowned throughout the Orthodox Jewish world. In this entirely Orthodox community, Hassidim are a small but growing minority.

Socio-Economic Status

Socio-economically, the Orthodox Jewish population is very mixed and does not necessarily reflect the same characteristics as the non-Jewish population within which they reside. All socio-economic groups are represented and families from both ends of the economic spectrum live side by side quite happily. Men may be engaged in many varied fields and all occupations are represented within the community, from the professions through to unskilled manual work. Orthodox Jews are somewhat restricted when seeking employment as for strict religious reasons they are unable to work on *Shabbos* (see Chapter 5). This means that not only may they not work on Saturdays, but in the winter months they need to leave early on Friday afternoons so as to be home before sunset. In previous decades there was a considerable amount of manufacturing industry based around North-east London and in the Manchester region and many Orthodox Jewish factory owners provided employment for other members of the community. This sector of industry has shrunk together with the traditional Jewish trades such as jewellery, clothing manufacture and property management. There is a large pool of part-time employment particularly for women, for as the community has grown, so has the number of schools and shops where there is a constant demand for part-time workers.

The cost of living for Orthodox Jews is higher than for other groups, for a number of reasons. Orthodox Jewish families tend to be larger than average. Also kosher food prices are generally significantly higher than non-kosher equivalents (due to the additional costs of manufacture and supervision). Furthermore, almost all education from pre-school to adult is privately funded. Many families also contribute to the costs of running their synagogue, which may include a rabbi's salary. In addition, because of the need to live within walking distance of synagogues (due to the restriction on travel on *Shabbos*), the cost of housing, whether rented or purchased, attracts a premium, so adding to the cost of living.

Unemployment has taken its toll and in many families the main breadwinner may not be able to find employment. Most unemployed Orthodox men will spend much of the day in the synagogue engaged in private study or joining in study groups (*kollel*) or attending lectures (*shiurim*). Pastimes and recreational activities rarely find place in the daily routine.

There is a reluctance on the part of Orthodox Jews to attend non-Jewish training colleges or universities, but an increasing number of single sex courses are available within the community, offering training in computer skills and business management among other subjects.

There is reasonably good support within the community and less well off families may often be helped by others in better circumstances (see *Care & Support Within the Community* – Chapter 8). Better off families may live surprisingly modestly and low income families may make the most of their resources, so that outwardly it may be quite hard to judge a family's economic status simply by looking at their appearance or housing.

Housing requirements relate to the need to be within walking distance of synagogues (as travel other than on foot is forbidden on *Shabbos*), as well as for access to the Orthodox Jewish Schools and shops and the need for large family units. There is a mixture of owner occupied and rented accommodation. Some areas with large Orthodox Jewish communities now have their own Housing Associations.

CHAPTER 2

THE TRADITIONAL WAY OF LIFE

Insularity (Being Different)

The Hassidic community deliberately try to insulate themselves from the secular outside world and its influences as much as possible. They maintain their traditional distinctive dress they speak their own language, Yiddish, and they keep contact with the outside world to a necessary minimum. They do not have televisions in their homes, many do not even listen to the radio and apart from newspapers specifically aimed at their own community most Hassidim do not read the national press. As a consequence they may be unaware of national healthcare campaigns such as immunisations drives or health promotion programmes.

Dress

The most obvious distinguishing feature of Hassidic Jews is their distinctive way of dressing. Most Hassidim still adhere to the traditional garb of Eastern Europe dating back to the eighteenth century. This is seen as being important, in that it singles out the Hassidic population and identifies them as a distinct entity and a separate community. There are some variations in the dress style of the different Hassidic groups.

Traditionally, Orthodox Jewish men will keep their heads covered at all times as a constant reminder that they are in the presence of God. Outdoors, they usually wear hats under which they have a skullcap for indoor wear. The skullcap *('kappel'* or *'yarmulke')* is worn at all times and most men will only remove it for bathing. Some men may have a special *kappel* for wearing in bed, and they may want to keep it on when admitted to hospital. Adjusting a slipped head-covering for an ill patient would be appreciated, as this would enable a man to maintain his dignity. Many men grow sidelocks known as *'payos'*. Some Hassidic groups never trim their *payos,* whereas other groups may cut them when they grow beyond a certain length. *Payos* are left long and dangling by some groups, but others will tuck them away behind their ears or under their skullcaps or hats. Some groups do not cut their boys' hair until their third birthday. There is a prohibition in Jewish law against men using a razor blade on the beard area. Almost all Hassidic men grow beards and most don't even trim them. There are many Orthodox men who use electric shavers, which are permitted. Men wear a special garment called a *tallis koton* at all times. This is a four cornered garment worn over or under the shirt with *tzitzis* (tassels) on each corner.

Women tend to dress in a modest style. They do not expose much bare skin and even in summer will wear their sleeves and skirts long, their necklines high and their legs covered with stockings or tights. Most Orthodox Jewish women do not wear trousers. According to Jewish law, married women must cover their hair at all times. The exact nature of the head-covering varies between different Orthodox Jewish groups. Some women wear headscarves or hats, others wear wigs and yet others wigs as well as hats. Many women will keep their own hair under their head-covering, sometimes at full length, while amongst some Hassidic groups all the hair may be shaved off. It is important to maintain a woman's dignity, when in hospital or in a residential home especially in situations where her head-covering might slip.

Female healthcare workers working closely within the Orthodox Jewish community need to be sensitive to this dress code, especially if their work takes them into peoples homes. Although they will not be expected to don Hassidic garb, they will be made more welcome if they wear long sleeves, skirts covering their knees and high necklines.

Language

Whereas most of the Orthodox Jewish population speak good English, there are many Hassidic groups for whom English is a second language. An increasing number of the Hassidic community are going back to using Yiddish as a first language and some of the younger children may not be able to communicate in English until they learn it in school. Yiddish is a language of early medieval central European origin and has been spoken by Eastern European Jews for many centuries. It is a very rich and expressive language and is not to be confused with Hebrew, the classical form of which is reserved by Orthodox Jews for sacred purposes such as prayer and religious study. (Modern Hebrew by contrast is the everyday language of modern Israel and is hardly spoken by the Hassidic community.)

Healthcare workers may encounter language problems when dealing with the Hassidic community, especially with children or the very elderly. These include situations such as when Health Visitors are performing developmental assessments on young children or during audiological testing, or district nurses caring for the elderly at home. A particular problem is speech therapy, especially as there are no Yiddish speaking speech therapists available in the relevant districts. Communication with reception and medical staff in doctors' surgeries or in hospitals may be a problem and as with any other group, staff need to be extra patient. Even those who do speak English well may be unfamiliar with the names of parts of the body, as their knowledge of biology and anatomical terms might be poor.

Names and Dates of Birth

A problem commonly encountered by healthcare workers relates to patients' names and dates of birth. All Orthodox Jews are given a Hebrew name. In addition, many Jews will also be given a traditional English type name on their birth certificates. These English names are sometimes direct equivalents of the Hebrew name e.g. *Yakov* and Jacob, *Dovid* and David or *Shloime* and Solomon but some groups register an English name which may have no relationship at all to the Hebrew name. Yet others, may only have a Hebrew name and use this transliterated as their registered name on their birth certificates. It should be noted that personal names as recorded on birth certificates are 'first' names or 'forenames' or even 'registered' names but never 'Christian' names!

Traditionally, boys are named at the *bris* (circumcision) ceremony on the eighth day of life. This may cause problems where the *bris* is delayed. When this delay is protracted, such as when the infant is unwell, a name might be allocated which is changed or added to when the *bris* does eventually take place.

Girls are named within a few days of birth when the father attends a brief synagogue ceremony.

Not only might healthcare workers encounter difficulties with the spelling or pronunciation of first names, but it is also not unusual to come across a Jewish patient who is so used to using his Hebrew name that he might not even remember his registered name. This may lead to misunderstandings when booking appointments and with the filing of patients' records. Since first names are often given in memory of deceased relatives, it is not unusual to find several cousins in an extended family sharing the same first name and surname when they have been called after a common grandparent, leading to obvious confusion! It may be necessary to check dates of birth when booking appointments.

Many Orthodox Jews use the Hebrew calendar in their day to day lives and therefore similar problems may be encountered when asking patients their date of birth. The Hebrew calendar is based on the lunar year, as opposed to the solar year on which the secular calendar is based. This means that there is some fluctuation between dates in the two systems and dates such as those of birthdays and festivals may be out by a week or more in different years. The Hebrew calendar has an extra 'leap month' every few years, so as to bring it back into alignment with the solar calendar. Conversion charts and computer programmes are readily available to convert Hebrew calendar dates.

Addressing People

As a general rule the best policy for non-Jewish healthcare workers is to address adults using the standard English Mr, Mrs or Miss followed by the surname, (or Rabbi, where appropriate). Children are best addressed by their first names.

The Family and Home

The family is seen as being central to the Orthodox Jewish traditional way of life. Much as "an Englishman's home is his castle", there are many Hassidic groups who feel uncomfortable at letting non-Jewish people into their homes, even if they are healthcare workers such as Health Visitors. Healthcare workers should not take this as a personal affront, nor should they be offended by this attitude. In many cases, advance notification such as by telephone to arrange a visit at a mutually acceptable time or even at the healthcare worker's own place of work, may be advisable.

Each door (other than toilets and bathrooms) in an Orthodox Jewish home or workplace will have a *mezuzah* attached to the door post at shoulder height. This contains a small parchment scroll on which is written the *Shema* (a passage from the bible containing the fundamentals of Jewish beliefs). Some people have the custom to touch or kiss them each time they walk through a doorway.

Because Jewish dietary laws (see Chapter 3) require meat and milk dishes to be kept apart, a healthcare worker given a cup of tea in an Orthodox Jewish home may be asked not to put it down on a surface used for meat dishes.

Synagogue ('Shul'), Prayer and Study

There are many synagogues (*'Shuls'*) in the Stamford Hill area providing for all the different subgroups found within the

Orthodox and Hassidic community. Some are housed in large, purpose-built buildings; others are in converted houses; whereas some are very small informal *'Shtibelech'* ('prayer rooms'). Most of the large Hassidic groups have their own synagogues, which are often the focal point or base for that particular group.

Prayer is very central to the Orthodox Jewish way of life. Prayers are recited three times a day in Classical (Biblical) Hebrew. Festivals and special Holydays are marked by additional synagogue services.

The synagogue is much more than a place of worship. It is also a place of study and a meeting place; for many men it represents the pivot of their daily lives. Men spend a considerable amount of time in the synagogue, engaged in prayer and study.

Most Orthodox Jewish men spend some time most days in the study of Jewish law, either on their own or in groups. Women spend far less time in the synagogue, many only attending occasionally on *Shabbos* or on *Yom-Tov* (festivals).

For the morning service, men don a *tallis* (a prayer shawl with *tzitzis* – tassels on each of the four corners) and other than on *Shabbos* and *Yom-Tov* (festivals), *tefillin* (leather boxes containing the *shema* [see above, *mezuzah*] and other scriptural verses) on the arm and forehead. It is extremely important to Orthodox Jewish men not to omit putting on *tallis* and *tefillin* for even one day.

Whilst praying, men may make rhythmical swaying rocking movements of the trunk and at certain points they will bow forward. Although some parts of the service are meant to be said standing, an ill patient would be able to pray whilst seated or lying in bed. An ill patient who cannot go to the synagogue would always try to make every effort to pray at home, or in hospital. Consideration should be given to Jewish hospital patients who request privacy in order to pray. This is particularly important in hospital wards, where there are incontinent patients, as it is forbidden to pray in such an environment. Similarly, Orthodox Jewish patients may not be able to pray in mixed wards. Simple measures, such as pulling the bedside curtains to, may enable a patient to say his prayers. Inability to pray at the right time might result in considerable distress, and a little courtesy and forethought may be appreciated and would contribute in very large measure to a patient's comfort in hospital. There are a few sections of prayer where interruption is strictly forbidden and the worshipper might appear to ignore someone who tries to interrupt him at such times. Nurses, doctors and other healthcare workers should not take offence at this.

Healthcare workers may find clients reluctant to book appointments if these coincide with prayer or study periods. Women may want to arrange their appointments around their husbands' prayer and study times so that their husbands are free to baby sit.

Bar -Mitzvah

In Jewish law a boy reaches the age of majority at the age of thirteen when he becomes *'bar-mitzvah'* ('an adult required to keep the *mitzvos'* – the religious laws). A girl becomes *'bas-mitzvah'* at twelve. From then on the child is regarded as a full adult for the purposes of Jewish law and religious practice including observances such as fasting on the fast days and for boys, putting on *Tefillin* daily. In the Hassidic community a *bar-mitzvah* is a relatively low key affair, the occasion being marked by a celebratory meal for family and friends and a small synagogue ceremony, whereas for girls there is usually no public celebration.

Education

The Orthodox and Hassidic communities have their own schools and many of the larger Hassidic groups have their own full time education facilities for their own children, almost all of which are entirely funded by the parents and the wider community. All children go to kindergarten from the age of three and the system carries pupils right through to full time adult further (religious) education. The sexes are segregated right from the start and most of the teaching is conducted in Yiddish. Hebrew reading is taught quite young and the standard of literacy in Hebrew and Yiddish is extremely high. In fact illiteracy due other than to illness or handicap is unknown in the Orthodox Jewish community. In their early teens, most young men go away from home to study in a *Yeshiva* (full time college), where they study the *Talmud* and other aspects of Jewish life and Jewish law. After leaving school, many of the girls go on to full time further education at seminaries. Some girls may go away from home for a year or so for these studies. All adults will devote some time each day to religious study. There are a number of men who continue full time study and research throughout their lives at institutes of higher religious study (*Kollel*), of which there are a growing number.

Rabbis

The title Rabbi (pl. *Rabbonim*) literally means 'teacher'. In its most commonly used sense the title is applied to the spiritual leader of a community. Many large synagogues have a full-time rabbi. Smaller communities might have a rabbi on a part-time basis and yet others may have someone acting in that capacity on an honorary basis. The rabbi's role includes officiating in synagogue services, solemnising weddings, attending circumcisions and other celebrations as well as officiating at funerals when necessary. In addition, most rabbis conduct *Shiurim* (lectures or study sessions). Many rabbis will also rule on matters of Jewish law (*Halocha*) and most are freely available for consultation even at short notice. A rabbi attached to a rabbinic court is given the title *Dayan* 'judge' (pl. *Dayonim*). There are some experienced rabbis to whom people will turn for guidance and advice on all sorts of matters.

There may be occasions when problems need discussion with a rabbi and a healthcare worker may need to liaise directly with a rabbi. Most rabbis will be happy to discuss problems over the phone and are generally easily accessible. A rabbi should be addressed simply as 'Rabbi' or as 'Rabbi Cohen' (or whatever his surname). A *Dayan* would similarly be addressed as 'Dayan' or 'Dayan Cohen' (for example). The title rabbi is also often used as term of respect, such as to teachers or possibly to elderly learned members of the community.

The title '*Reb*' together with the *first* name (e.g. *Reb Duvid*) is often used as a term of respect and approximates to the use of 'Mister' in English. Non-Jewish people are best advised to stick to the English standard Mr or Mrs, or whatever the case may be.

Etiquette

Although, "when in Rome do as the Romans do" is an important maxim in the British way of life, it is important for healthcare workers to understand that there are certain aspects of the Hassidic way of life which are of fundamental importance to members of that community and which many of them will not give up or change, even for politeness' sake.

Physical contact between members of the opposite sex, except between parents and their children and between siblings, is strictly avoided. As a consequence there are a number of instances where this may be of relevance to healthcare workers. For example, many Orthodox Jews will not shake hands with members of the opposite sex. This should not be taken as an act of rudeness but rather as an important aspect of Orthodox Jewish cultural behaviour. Many Orthodox Jewish patients might feel uncomfortable by the well intentioned and common practice whereby a doctor or nurse places a hand on a patient to provide comfort and reassurance. Of course, where physical contact is necessary and unavoidable in strictly clinical situations there are no restrictions. For example, there would be no problems at all with a male obstetrician delivering a baby with all the physical (and even intimate) contact that that involves. However, a congratulatory pat on the arm or a reassuring hand on the shoulder gesture, following the delivery might make the woman feel rather uncomfortable. Because of the restriction on physical contact, some members of the community may not even pass objects directly to a member of the opposite sex, but will put them down first. This again should not cause offence in situations such as when reception staff hand prescriptions to patients or when giving change for the waiting room pay phone.

There is a prohibition against being secluded with a member of the opposite sex and there may be situations where this could cause problems. For example, a patient in hospital may not wish to be alone in a lift with an escorting nurse when being moved from one department to another and he may ask the nurse to wait until a third person comes along. A patient may ask a doctor or healthcare worker of the opposite sex to leave the door unlocked or even slightly open when being interviewed. Again, these requests should not cause offence; they are important to the patient or client as religious requirements and are not in any way directed personally at the healthcare workers themselves.

Where possible, healthcare workers such as district nurses who visit patients or clients at home should be of the same sex as their patients or clients. On the whole, most Orthodox Jewish women will not mind seeing a male doctor, although if given the option they may prefer a woman doctor particularly when a physical examination is required. Where the presenting problem is gynaecological in nature, they might feel more comfortable talking to a woman doctor. Many Orthodox Jewish men would not be happy to see a female doctor and might even refuse to see her, preferring to wait for a male doctor to become available.

In recent years, problems have arisen when Orthodox Jewish patients have been admitted to mixed sex hospital wards. Orthodox Jews may find this extremely uncomfortable or even distressing and indeed they may be reluctant to be admitted for this reason. This problem is even more marked in psychiatric units where patients are generally physically well and are encouraged to socialise and mix freely. Hospital managers must be sensitive to these feelings and should make provision for some degree of separate sex accommodation where appropriate. According to the NHS Patient's Charter all patients can expect their "privacy, dignity and cultural and religious beliefs to be respected". In relation to hospital admission, the charter also states "If you prefer a single-sex ward, your wishes will be respected where possible".

Because the sexes tend to be segregated in their daily lives, some Orthodox or Hassidic Jews may feel uncomfortable if seated between members of the opposite sex in situations such as at meetings. Arranging the seating with men and women on opposite sides of the table (or room) would be appreciated.

CHAPTER 3
DIETARY LAWS

Diet

One of the best known characteristics of the Jewish religion is the observance of a *kosher* diet. The word 'kosher' means 'fit (to eat)' and food that is forbidden is known as *'treifeh'*. (Literally the word means 'torn' and it originally referred to animals killed other than in the kosher manner – it is now used to refer to any food that is not kosher.)

Orthodox Jews adhere strictly to a kosher diet, that is, a diet which complies with the Jewish dietary laws and which is rigorously observed in considerable detail. Observing *'kashrus'* – ('kosherness') is seen as being extremely important and is seen as a form of holiness and self discipline.

Briefly, the main and most basic rules of kashrus can be summarised as follows:-

• Only certain species of animal or fowl may be eaten. These must be slaughtered and prepared in a very specific way before they can be eaten. Animals are slaughtered in a such a way that they are killed as humanely as possible. Before it can be cooked, the meat must be soaked and salted in a very specific way to remove as much blood as possible. Therefore, not only must these products be purchased in a kosher shop, but they must also be prepared and cooked in an entirely kosher kitchen, to be acceptable.

• Kosher food may only be prepared or processed with utensils which have never been previously been used for *treifah* (non-kosher) foodstuffs. Preparing or even just re-heating on *treifah* cookware, may render kosher food *treifah* ('unkosher').

• Meat and dairy produce, or foods containing them, must not be prepared, cooked nor eaten together. They must also be kept completely apart in the kitchen to the extent that separate utensils are required to be used for meat and milk dishes. A strictly kosher kitchen will have two of everything – two sets of pots and pans, crockery, cutlery and kitchen utensils and if possible two sinks and draining boards, one being used for meat foods and the other for dairy foods. If space is at a premium the housewife will cover the work surfaces when changing from preparing meat or milk containing meals. Meat and milk dishes are not served at the same meal and after eating a meat meal, a minimum period of three hours must elapse before milk can be taken (many people wait for up to six hours before consuming dairy products after a meat meal). Invalids may be given rabbinical dispensation to reduce this time interval, if necessary. The interval after which meat foods can be consumed following dairy foods is very much shorter, the exact time depending on individual custom or tradition.

• Food such as fish, fruit or vegetables, which contain nothing of meat or dairy origin, are known as '*parev*' (neutral). These foods can be consumed with either a meat or dairy meal provided of course, that they have not previously been cooked together with meat or dairy foods.

- All fruits and vegetables are kosher, but as Orthodox Jews are strictly forbidden to eat insects they will be very particular to ensure that fruits and vegetables are completely free of infestation. Certain green products, such as brussel sprouts, are generally avoided, as it is extremely difficult to ensure that they are absolutely free of infestation.

- As with meat, only certain species of fish may be eaten. Seafood such as eels, crabs and shellfish are '*treifah*'. Unless the species is clearly recognisable, fish is only purchased from a kosher fishmonger.

- Only the milk of kosher species of animal may be drunk. The milk used by Orthodox Jews is milked and bottled under the supervision of a kashrus authority. Orthodox Jews will usually not drink unsupervised milk. However invalids may be given rabbinical dispensation to drink unsupervised milk. The rennet used in the manufacture of cheese must be kosher.

- The ingredients of all drinks and beverages must also be kosher. This does not present much problem for tea or coffee (although the rules for milk apply as above). Most soft or fruit drinks and most alcoholic drinks are permitted. However, wine and grape juice and their derivatives are an exception and may only be drunk if produced under the supervision of a kashrus authority and usually only if the *hechsher* seal (see next section) is intact.

- All mineral products and chemicals derived from them are kosher.

- Some commonly used food or drink additives, particularly colourings, stabilisers and emulsifiers may be derived from non-kosher sources and would thus be forbidden.

The observance of the laws of *kashrus* is extremely important and there are a number of rabbinical authorities who supervise the manufacture of kosher foodstuffs and who grant licences to butchers, restaurants and food manufacturers. Such a license is called a *hechsher* and is normally printed on the wrapping or packets of supervised foods. It is often present in the form of a small inconspicuous logo, identifying the particular rabbinical authority granting the licence.

Many Orthodox groups will only eat manufactured foods that have a *hechsher*. Some individuals may be more selective and might eat certain unsupervised products which are known never to contain non-kosher ingredients. Yet other groups will be highly specific and will only use products given a *hechsher* by a certain rabbinical authority and will not use products supervised by other authorities. These variations and preferences may confuse healthcare workers, particularly those working with hospital inpatients where certain foods may be acceptable to one patient, yet not to another. These variations should be respected as they may be quite important to the individual, who may have difficulty in explaining his particular preferences.

Healthcare professionals should understand how important and fundamental the observance of kashrus is to the Orthodox Jewish individual and community. Many Orthodox

Jews may not even accept a cup of tea prepared in a non-kosher kitchen and no offence should be taken when this is refused. Similarly, when a child is stopped by a parent from accepting a sweet that might be offered, say by a nurse after having been given an injection. (A supply of clearly labelled kosher [sugar-free] sweets might be appreciated!)

Kashrus and Health

The nutritional state of the Orthodox Jewish community is generally very good. In many areas kosher Meals on Wheels are available for the elderly or infirm and can be arranged through the local Social Services department. For hospital inpatients, strictly kosher meals are available through the Hospital Kosher Meals Service. These meals are supplied to the hospital in pre-packed sealed containers and are kept frozen in the hospital kitchen freezers. When requested by an Orthodox Jewish patient, the meal is defrosted and reheated in an oven or microwave whilst still in the sealed container. The meal is delivered to the patient with the seal intact. There is no objection to kosher food being handled by non-Jewish staff or carers.

Generally speaking, all food or dietary additives or indeed anything intended to be swallowed, when supplied for healthy individuals, must contain only kosher ingredients (for example vitamin supplements for healthy babies).

When possible, medication should also contain no non-kosher ingredients. It is not commonly realised that many medicines contain ingredients that are not kosher and in many circumstances these may present problems for members of the Orthodox Jewish community.

The following 'problem' ingredients may be encountered as they, or their derivatives, are present in a large range of medication:-

Glycerine – A sweet tasting liquid added to many medications (especially children's medicines) to make them palatable. It may be derived from animal (usually non-kosher) or vegetable (usually kosher) sources. Patients might request a doctor to prescribe a product where the source is known to be of vegetable origin. (For example 'Medinol', when a children's paracetamol suspension is required).

Lactose – A sweet tasting sugar derived from milk as a by-product of the cheese making process, which is present in a wide range of tablets where it is used as a bulking agent, being also used to make chewable and suckable tablets more palatable. Because it is a milk derivative, it presents problems with respect to the laws of milk and meat and also with respect to the requirements for the supervision of milk.

Gelatine – A tasteless substance used in the manufacture of many capsules and sometimes used in powder form in tablets. It is usually of animal origin (although synthetic sources do exist).

In addition, the Passover (*Pesach*) festival presents other problems relating to medicines. During the week of *Pesach,* Jews are strictly forbidden to eat any 'leavened' foods (that is, food containing flour that has 'risen'). Medicines containing wheat starch or any of its derivatives will present problems prior to and during the week of *Pesach.*

The laws governing products derived from non-kosher substances are complex but there are many situations where medications containing these ingredients might be permitted. Individual patients may wish to discuss specific cases with a rabbinical authority before using certain medications.

In general, the laws of Kashrus apply only to foods or substances that are ingested by mouth. Parenteral drugs (injectable or rectal preparations) are usually acceptable whatever their origin, so for example, insulin of pork or beef origin would be totally acceptable. There are no restrictions on the parenteral use of blood products and blood transfusions are unreservedly permitted, (as is blood donation). Hospitals in areas with Orthodox Jewish patients are becoming increasingly aware of the need to keep stocks of Kosher medicines.

A very high proportion of infants are breast fed, but where a formula substitute is required, this should be one known to contain no non-kosher ingredients. There are now several baby milk formulas available made under supervision and which have a *hechsher*.

Jewish law makes it clear that in life-threatening conditions, the laws of Kashrus (and indeed most other laws) can be set aside. Except in the most critical circumstances this should only be done with rabbinical guidance.

Hygiene

Hygiene is central to the Orthodox Jewish way of life and many religious activities may only be performed in a clean state. Even if their hands are 'socially' clean, Orthodox Jews will wash their hands in a ritual manner and recite a special *brocha* (blessing) on waking up after sleep, after going to the toilet and before meals (especially when bread is served). The washing is mostly done by pouring water over the hands from a cup. Some people will also wash their hands before praying. When bed-bound, Orthodox Jews may request a bowl and cup to wash their hands before eating or praying or after using a bed pan, even if their hands appear to be completely clean.

Many men will attend the *mikveh* (ritual bath house) on a regular (even daily) basis for ritual immersion. Bathing in the *mikveh* is purely for ritual purposes and is usually preceded by a shower or bath.

CHAPTER 4

MARRIAGE, SEX AND RELATED TOPICS

Marriage

The Hassidic way of life does not encourage young people to mix with members of the opposite sex. The sexes are segregated from an early age, even nursery schools are single sex. Hassidic couples tend to marry relatively young, the girls at about 18 and the boys at 20 or so. Marriages are not arranged as such, but couples are brought together by arranged introductions. The decision of whether to marry is entirely up to the young couple themselves; indeed Jewish law does not permit marriages between unwilling parties. According to Jewish law, both parties must be Jewish in order to marry. Although Jewish law does allow for divorce, the divorce rate is still relatively low and most marriages seem very happy. Domestic violence involving physical or psychological abuse (or child abuse) is rarely encountered within the Orthodox Jewish community. Where problems do arise within a marriage, couples are quite likely to seek help and advice from a rabbi or close relative and there are good facilities within the Orthodox Jewish and Hassidic community for marriage guidance (and other) counselling.

Traditionally the wedding ceremony takes place out of doors. Married women wear wedding rings, most men do not. Orthodox Jewish women start to cover their hair from the time of the wedding. In addition to wearing the traditional *bekishe* (shiny long black jacket), Hassidic men start to wear the *shtreimel* (round fur hat) on *Shabbos* and festival only after they are married.

Although young couples may get considerable social support from their extended families, they are nevertheless encouraged to live independent lives; so that even where a young couple live quite close to their parents (as many do) they would have their own accommodation.

Sexual Relations

Sex is regarded as a very private matter and will not be discussed freely. Sexual intercourse, within marriage is viewed as a positive, joyous and pleasurable act and in Jewish Law a husband is obliged to ensure that his wife enjoys sexual fulfilment. Orthodox Jewish schools do not provide sex education, but prior to marriage, individual guidance is given on a private one-to-one basis by an experienced 'marriage tutor' of the same sex. Where appropriate, and only then, healthcare workers should approach the subject cautiously and in a respectful manner. Unsolicited advice, such as on contraception, given by Health Visitors and midwives, may result in alienation of clients or patients. Tact is required to give clients or patients the opportunity to discuss these subjects where appropriate. The names of parts of the body are likely to be unfamiliar.

Intercourse is forbidden during menstruation or any uterine bleeding (*niddah*) and for seven days thereafter. Seven days after bleeding has ceased, the woman goes to the *mikveh* (ritual bath house) following which intercourse is again permitted. If possible, routine gynaecological procedures should be deferred until the next period or just after bleeding has ceased. It is not uncommon for an Orthodox Jewish woman to consult a doctor or nurse in order to determine the source of vaginal blood loss, to ascertain whether the bleeding is uterine in origin (*niddah*) or whether it is due to local irritation, such as from thrush (and therefore not *niddah*). Following any gynaecological examination, women may enquire whether there has been any contact bleeding even if only a small amount. During the time when a woman is a *niddah*, all forms of physical contact between husband and wife are forbidden. Couples will not hand objects directly to each other, but they will put things down for the other one to pick up. (As previously mentioned, some *Hassidic* people will never directly hand an object to a member of the opposite sex.)

The women's immersion in the *mikveh* is performed for ritual, not for hygiene purposes, indeed one must be completely clean beforehand and therefore immersion in the *mikveh* is preceded by a wash and soak in a bath. In order for the immersion to be valid, it is essential that all parts of the body come into direct contact with the *mikveh* water. Wound dressings, skin sutures, some prostheses or even temporary dental fillings may invalidate the immersion by preventing the water coming into contact with the body, forming a *chatzitzah* (a barrier or intervening substance). Patients may request that nonessential minor surgery or dental treatment is arranged so as not to interfere with the timing of their visit to the *mikveh* and where possible this request should be accommodated. The technical rules of what constitutes a *chatzitzah* are quite complex and occasionally a rabbi might need to be consulted for a ruling. He in turn may wish to discuss this with the doctor before reaching a decision.

Orthodox Jews are very strict in their observance of these laws (the 'Laws of Family Purity') and although they may seem hard for non-Jews to understand, respect and consideration will be greatly appreciated. There may be occasions when a couple might consult a rabbi about these intimate matters and he in turn may wish to discuss them with the medical practitioner concerned.

The *niddah* laws have some implications for patient management in a number of clinical areas. Women may occasionally request medication in order to defer their periods, particularly at holiday times, either so as to ensure that they do not have a period whilst on holiday, or if they are travelling to places where they do not have access to a *mikveh*. Similarly, doctors may be requested to arrange menstrual manipulation for a bride before her wedding. Orthodox Jewish menopausal women requesting treatment for climacteric symptoms may be reluctant to take any form of hormone replacement therapy (HRT) which would necessitate re-commencement of menstruation. There are further implications of the *niddah* laws which are of relevance to childbirth and infertility treatment, these are discussed in the relevant sections below.

Orthodox Jews are strictly monogamous and extramarital (including premarital) sex is absolutely forbidden. Sexually transmitted diseases (although not unheard of) are extremely rare, as is HIV infection and AIDS. Homosexual relationships are forbidden and where these do occur within the Orthodox community they will usually be conducted with utmost secrecy. Extreme sensitivity and assurance of confidentiality is required when dealing with issues of sexuality and sexual variation in Orthodox Jewish individuals.

Contraception

The family is central to the Jewish way of life and many Orthodox Jewish families are quite large. Marriage is almost universal and having a family and bringing up children is considered to be extremely important. Within the Orthodox Jewish communities a married couple are encouraged to "be fruitful and multiply", except where there is a good reason not to. Nevertheless, Judaism's attitude to contraception is somewhat more liberal than some other religions.

Many couples might choose to space their families by relying on the relative contraceptive effect of breast feeding, which although not by any means a reliable form of contraception, does reduce relative fertility for some months in many women.

A couple might consider using contraception where, for example, a woman's physical or mental health might be compromised by a (further) pregnancy. Many couples will only use contraception if they have received approval from a rabbi and often after an initial medical consultation, a woman may go away to consult her husband who will possibly want to discuss it with a rabbi first.

Where contraception is used, there is a hierarchy as to which methods are the most acceptable. According to Jewish law the oral contraceptive pill is the method of first choice. Where the pill is unsuitable or contraindicated then the IUCD or diaphragm may be acceptable. Condoms are not acceptable in Jewish law. Vasectomy is strictly forbidden, whereas tubal ligation may occasionally be permitted for instance where a pregnancy would be life threatening. In addition to using the natural relative contraceptive effect of breast feeding to space families, some couples may practice the rhythm or other 'natural' methods of family planning, but most rabbinical opinions would prefer the pill where contraception is indicated. Contraceptive injections, although acceptable as an alternative to the oral contraceptive pill do have the disadvantage of causing irregular and unpredictable uterine bleeding which may cause *niddah* problems. (The same is true of the newer progesterone impregnated IUCDs and to a much lesser extent, the progesterone only pill)

Abortions may be permitted in rare circumstances, such as when the mother's life would be endangered by continuing the pregnancy. Where permitted, the procedure should be carried out as early as possible in the pregnancy.

Childbirth

There are a number of specific issues surrounding childbirth which affect Orthodox Jewish couples. Because abortions are generally forbidden other than for reasons of danger to the mother's life, women may be reluctant to undergo certain screening tests and procedures where the only practical outcome would be the offer of a termination of the pregnancy (e.g. tests for Down's syndrome). Obviously, where there is the possibility of useful, practical therapeutic intervention then screening tests would be encouraged (e.g. screening for hydronephrosis). When offering screening tests the indications and the practical outcome possibilities should be discussed with the woman who may want to discuss it with her husband, her GP or even her rabbi, before reaching a decision.

Because of the relatively large size of families, women may be reluctant to undergo caesarean sections unless absolutely clinically indicated, as this often limits the number of subsequent pregnancies. Of course where there is any question of risk to the mother's or infant's life, caesarean section would be accepted without question. Induction of labour for other than sound clinical indications involving risk to the mother or infant may be an issue for some Orthodox Jewish women. This is because some Orthodox Jewish and especially some *Hassidic* groups have strong feeling about babies arriving at the most auspicious time that has been predetermined for them; induction might be seen as interfering with this. Where possible, elective procedures should be timed to avoid *Shabbos* or *Yom-Tov*.

A women is considered to be a *niddah* (see previous sections) from the onset of established labour, throughout labour and during the postnatal period until she goes to the *mikveh* seven days after all uterine blood loss has ceased. This has a number of practical implications. Physical contact between husband and wife is forbidden, so that during labour he is unable to hold her hand or rub her back. Some husbands may wish to remain in the delivery room whereas others might want to sit nearby, possibly reciting *Tehillim* (Psalms). Some husbands will remain until the second stage but will then leave the room for the actual delivery. Many women find it easier to have a female relative or friend with them during labour. There is a voluntary womens' organisation ('Labour Support') which provides 'Labour Supporters' and who will, if needed, stay with Orthodox Jewish women throughout labour. They have been trained in the techniques of breathing and pain relieving methods and are very supportive. Some hospitals also have Orthodox Jewish maternity liaison workers. Because of *niddah* restrictions on physical contact between a couple, they might not display the expected usual intimacy straight after a birth. Observers unused to this must remember that this is not a reflection of the couple's relationship, but is a religious constraint.

As with all restrictions in Jewish law, those discussed above in relation to obstetric care are set aside wherever there is any risk to maternal, foetal or infant life.

Infertility

Because so much of the Jewish way of life revolves around the family and because having children is so central to the Jewish way of life, infertility is considered to be a major handicap. Jewish couples may go to extraordinary lengths to obtain help with infertility problems, even where medical opinion might regard them as 'hopeless' cases. It is important for healthcare workers in this area to be sensitive to these feelings when counselling these couples. Because larger than average families are the norm, Orthodox Jewish couples may request help for secondary infertility and this needs sensitive handling by infertility workers, especially where resources are limited and secondary infertility is not regarded as an important problem.

Treatment for infertility may be complicated by some aspects of Jewish law such as the laws of *niddah* or *Shabbos* and *Yom-Tov*. No matter how distressing their infertility, a couple may not be willing to set aside or transgress such fundamental principles of Jewish law. Where possible, these issues should be handled sensitively and efforts made to accommodate the couple's needs and feelings. For example, where a couple are involved in an *in-vitro* fertilisation (IVF) programme, it may be necessary to time treatment cycles to take account of these important aspects of an Orthodox Jewish couple's life. It may be necessary to liaise closely with a rabbi with a special interest in this area.

Infertile couples may wish to adopt a child or two and indeed adoption is considered to be a great *mitzvah* (meritorious act or good deed). Orthodox Jewish couples will usually only want to adopt a child who is Jewish by birth but unfortunately for them there are not many of these available. There is however always a need for Orthodox Jewish foster parents. With the recent trend away from institutionalised care for children with special needs and the modern emphasis on community care, there are a small number of children with special needs who are available for adoption or fostering.

Cervical Smears

Statistically it has been shown that the Orthodox Jewish and Hassidic communities are amongst the lowest risk groups for cervical cancer in the world. (One could argue that this is all the more reason to encourage screening because as the risk is so low, the clinical index of suspicion is consequently reduced and a case would be more likely to go undetected.)

Because intercourse is forbidden following vaginal bleeding, women may be reluctant to have cervical smears, for although in most cases taking a smear does not cause any bleeding, there may occasionally be a small amount of contact bleeding from the cervix. In order to avoid any problems caused by the possibility of bleeding started by taking a smear, Orthodox Jewish women may time a smear to coincide with the end of a menstrual period. Flexibility and understanding will help to encourage high uptake rates for cervical screening programmes. Routine smears on pregnant women are best left to the postnatal examination or before intercourse has been resumed.

Breast Feeding

Unless there is a compelling reason not to, almost all Orthodox Jewish women breast feed their babies. However they will only do so in private and not in a public place. Even at home they will not feed openly (especially in mixed company), unless discreetly draped.

CHAPTER 5

SHABBOS AND FESTIVALS

Shabbos (The Sabbath)

According to Jewish teaching the *Shabbos* is the central pivot around which the rest of the week revolves and it is one of the most cherished fundamentals of Judaism. From the very beginning of the establishment of Judaism, the *Shabbos* has been set aside as a special day different from the rest of the week. It is a day of rest and freedom from the outside world, and a time of worship and study. *Shabbos* is truly a family day, with family meals at which the family joins in the singing of hymns and when discussion of Biblical texts or religious topics is a regular feature.

Shabbos begins on Friday evening at sundown and ends on Saturday night after nightfall. There is thus considerable seasonal variation, with *Shabbos* in London commencing as early as 3:30 p.m. in midwinter but as late as 9 p.m. in midsummer. The termination of *Shabbos* similarly varies between about 5 p.m. and 11 p.m. in London. Times in other locations vary with the latitude and of course seasonal variation must also allow for clock changes between summer and winter. There may also be some slight variation in these times between different Jewish groups.

Shabbos starts with the lighting of candles, usually by the women, when the men go to the synagogue for the Friday night service. If it is safe to light candles in hospital this is preferred, otherwise another member of the family will light them at home on behalf of the patient. This is followed by the traditional family meal which commences with *Kiddush* ('sanctification'), a special prayer said over a cup of wine or grape juice. At the meal traditional foods such as gefilte (chopped) fish, kugel (potato or pasta puddings) and other delicacies are eaten, which in Hassidic circles reflects their Eastern European origins.

· *Shabbos* morning starts with a synagogue service attended by the whole family, other than mothers of young children who are exempt. This is followed by a family meal at midday. The men will attend the synagogue again towards the end of the day, where they will meet to study and pray together or to hear a lecture by the rabbi. Often they will have a small communal meal towards dusk.

Shabbos ends after nightfall with *havdolah*, a short family ceremony, said over a cup of wine or grape juice. A plaited candle is lit and a spice box is passed around.

The traditional ceremonies and prayers are very important to Orthodox Jews and a patient in hospital or in a residential home should be afforded every possibility to be able to perform them as far as possible. Friends or relatives may come in to help perform these ceremonies for ill or debilitated patients. Elderly, confused or demented patients may find comfort in the *Shabbos* traditions and may become disorientated if they are omitted.

During *Shabbos,* Orthodox Jews do no *melocha* (that is creative 'work' as defined by Jewish law) nor engage in workaday activities. This includes writing, using the telephone, travelling by car or public transport, switching lights on or off, or using any electrical equipment. They do not touch money on *Shabbos*. Cooking is also forbidden and all food served on *Shabbos* must be prepared beforehand. Cooked food is kept hot on the stove from before *Shabbos*.

The prohibition on performing *melocha* is extremely strict and is a concept which is very difficult for non-Jews to understand. Orthodox Jews will go to extreme lengths to avoid transgressing the *Shabbos* laws which should not be ridiculed, no matter how irrational the laws may seem. Where possible Orthodox Jewish patients will try to avoid having to be in hospital on *Shabbos* but obviously on many occasions it will be unavoidable. When in hospital on *Shabbos*, Jewish patients may need help with doing things that are forbidden by Jewish law, such as switching lights on or off, or using a lift when using the stairs would not be possible. Even tearing toilet tissue on *Shabbos* is a *melocha*, therefore Orthodox Jewish patients will need to bring loose-leaf toilet tissue with them into hospital, if this is not provided. Turning a hot water tap on or off is similarly forbidden and a nurse may be asked to help run a bath .

Because carrying items into the street is considered to be *melocha,* patients who are admitted to hospital on *Shabbos*, such as a woman in labour, would not be able to carry their personal effects out to the ambulance and may ask the ambulance driver to do so for them even if the husband is in attendance. This should not cause offence, as it is not intended to demean but is a necessity because of the strict *Shabbos* laws. Patients who are discharged from hospital on *Shabbos* may wish to wait until after dark before leaving for home. According to Jewish law, one may not ask another Jew, even a non observant one, to do a *melocha* on *Shabbos*. Every courtesy should be extended to patients who are very strict about not transgressing the *Shabbos* laws and may become distressed if not assisted or if forced to break these strict laws, even if they may seem irrational or nonsensical.

Writing is a *melocha* and Orthodox Jewish patients would normally be unable to sign consent forms on *Shabbos* or *Yom-Tov* unless there is an immediate threat to life. Hospitals in areas with Orthodox Jewish patients might come to an arrangement whereby they accept verbal consent (possibly permitting a third party such as the surgeon or ward sister to sign on the patient's behalf) or agree to the patient or next of kin signing retrospectively after the end of *Shabbos*.

Recently, an organisation called *Ezra Umarpeh* ('Help and Healing') have established facilities at some London hospitals, in order that parents and carers might have food, hot drinks and religious requisites available if they need to stay with a patient at the hospital over *Shabbos*; this is especially useful if the patient is actually admitted on *Shabbos*.

In emergency life-threatening situations, the *Shabbos* laws are set aside and in many cases there may need to be consultation between patients, their families, rabbis and healthcare workers.

Although all *Shabbos* restrictions are set aside where there is any risk to life, most Orthodox Jews would wish to try to avoid being in hospital over *Shabbos* or *Yom-Tov* if at all possible. They may therefore be reluctant to schedule non-urgent routine admissions if it would mean being in over *Shabbos* or *Yom-Tov*. Even where this is unavoidable they may be reluctant to undergo non-essential investigations such as blood tests or X-ray examinations on these days. Some Orthodox Jewish patients may be reluctant to take non-essential medications on *Shabbos* and when prescribed medication on a long term basis, they may well enquire about the advisability of missing out one day's treatment each week. The application of creams and ointments directly onto the skin on *Shabbos* may present some problems and where essential may have to be performed either by a non-Jewish third party or by indirect application such as via a gauze swab.

Festivals (Yom-Tov)

There are several major religious festivals during the course of the Jewish calendar year. As with the *Shabbos,* these festivals commence before sunset on the preceding day and conclude after nightfall at the end of the festival. On *Yom-Tov*, as on *Shabbos,* most *melocha* is forbidden (with some technical differences). Most of the festivals are in paired days, which in effect is like having two days of *Shabbos* one after the other. (When the festivals fall close to a weekend, then together with *Shabbos* there could be three days in a row when most *melocha* is prohibited.) This has some implications for clinical workload, as on *Shabbos* and *Yom-Tov* patients will not attend for routine consultations, causing a rush beforehand and a build up afterwards. In addition, because the festivals are family occasions, there is often a great deal of travel around the festival times, with an associated increase in anxiety levels and consultation rates. These factors can cause quite a disruption to appointment systems, particularly around September time when a number of the festivals occur within the space of just over three weeks. Practices with a high proportion of Orthodox Jewish patients will need to anticipate this consultation pattern to accommodate patients' needs.

Each of the festivals has its own special significance, rituals and customs, the observance of which is important. There are even special foods associated with the different festivals. Hospital patients or elderly residents in residential homes will derive great comfort from being able to observe and participate in the various rituals and traditions as much as possible.

Rosh Hashona (New Year)

This generally falls during September. In contrast to the secular new year, it is a relatively solemn occasion. It lasts for two days which are largely spent in synagogue worship, praying for Divine blessing for the year ahead. One of the special features of *Rosh Hashona* is the blowing of the *shofar* (ceremonial ram's horn) during the synagogue service. Hospital patients or those in a residential homes would probably wish to hear the *shofar* being blown. *Rosh Hashona* together with *Yom Kippur* are often referred to as the "High Holydays" (*Yommin Noraim,* literally, 'days of awe') indicating the solemnity of these days and the time of year in general. Stress levels may be raised and consultation rates increased. Many Hassidic men travel, often abroad, to be with their *Rebbe* at this time of the year.

Yom Kippur (The Day of Atonement)

This, the most solemn and holy day in the Jewish calendar, falls ten days after *Rosh Hashona.* It is marked by a twenty five hour fast observed by all adults (girls over twelve and boys over thirteen). The day is spent entirely in synagogue worship. The fast of *Yom Kippur* is regarded as being so important and central to Judaism that even many Jews who may not otherwise be religiously observant will fast. Fasting is extremely important but exemptions may be given to those too ill or frail to be able to do so. Exemptions would be usually be given in discussion with a rabbi who may first wish to confer with the patient's medical attendants. Exemptions are often only partial and may involve eating small amounts of food or liquids at specified intervals. The taking of medication may be permitted. Essential medication will always be permitted, but often only following discussion with the doctor or rabbi or possibly even both. Elderly patients or invalids (such as diabetics) who have been advised not to fast may understandably be upset at not being able to fulfil what is a very important aspect of their Judaism, possibly for the first time in their adult lives. It may be necessary for a rabbinical advisor to explain and counsel them to help them come to terms with this and to accept this ruling. The rabbi may wish to discuss with the doctors the risks involved.

Succos

The *Succos* – 'Tabernacles' – festival also falls in the autumn, five days after *Yom Kippur* and is a joyous *Yom-Tov*. During this week long festival, meals are eaten in a *succah*, that is a temporary structure which has an open ceiling covered in leaves and branches. Many Orthodox men also sleep in the *succah*. A palm branch (*lulov*) and citron fruit (*esrog*) are used ceremonially during synagogue worship. Ill patients are generally excused from eating in a *succah* but they may have a *lulov* brought to them so as to enable them to perform that ceremony. On the first two and last two days *melocha* (work) is forbidden (similar to on *Shabbos*), but the interim days (*Chol Hamoed*), although still part of the festival, are less restrictive and are often used as a time of family holiday and outings. On these interim days, Orthodox and Hassidic patients continue to wear their festive *Shabbos* clothes even when going to the surgery or visiting hospitals.

Pesach (Passover)

This festival falls in the spring (and often coincides with Easter). Like *Succos*, it is also a week long festival with *Chol Hamoed* between the first two and last two days. The most significant feature of this festival is the very strict prohibition on the eating of *chometz* foods. *Chometz* is food which is made of, or which contains, any leaven or risen flour. *Matza* (unleavened crackers) are eaten instead of bread during the week of *Pesach*. On the first two nights of *Pesach*, families gather together for the *seder* ceremony, during which the story of the exodus from Egypt is read and discussed and at which a festive meal is served.

The prohibition on eating (and possessing) *chometz* on *Pesach* is extremely strict and Orthodox Jews will go to great lengths to ensure that there is no trace of *chometz* in their possession during the week of *Pesach*. The house is cleaned from top to bottom and a ritual search is made on the eve of *Pesach* to remove all traces of *chometz* from the home and Jewish owned workplaces. A separate set of kitchen utensils is used for *Pesach* and the normally strict dietary laws take on an added dimension. This may present problems relating to medicines which contain wheat starch or its derivatives, as these are *chometz*. Patients may enquire about suitable substitutes to use during the week of *Pesach*. The laws prohibiting *chometz* and their use in medicines are complex and medical staff may be contacted by rabbis to discuss individual patient's requirements over *Pesach*.

Shavuos

Shavuos – 'Pentecost' – is a two day festival which falls six weeks after *Pesach* (in the early summer). It commemorates the time when Moses received the *Torah* on Mount Sinai. The *Torah* is the sacred book on which all the teachings of Judaism are based.

Other Festivals

The Jewish calendar also has some minor festivals on which normal workaday activities are permitted, although most Orthodox Jews might try and take the day, or part of it, off work so as to be with their families, for what are essentially family occasions.

Chanukah

This festival (the 'Festival of Lights') falls in December and lasts for a week. Each evening at dusk there is a candle lighting ceremony. On the first evening a single candle is lit and this increases nightly until eight are lit on the last night. This is generally a happy family occasion, accompanied by the eating of traditional sweetmeats.

Purim

This is a one day festival which falls in the spring. It is a happy and joyous occasion on which the children (and some adults) dress up in fancy dress. Gifts of food are exchanged between family and friends and everyone has a great time!

Fast Days

Apart from *Yom Kippur* there are several other fasts. The most important of these is *Tisha B'av* ('the ninth day of the month of *Av'*) which falls in mid summer and commemorates the destruction of the Temple in Jerusalem. It is a twenty five hour fast and it is almost as strictly observed as *Yom Kippur,* except that *melocha* (work) is permitted. The rules on exemption from fasting are similar (but slightly more lenient) to those of *Yom Kippur*. It is a solemn day, on which people are supposed to dwell on the serious calamities that befell the Jewish people at the time of the destruction of the Temple, as well as the many tragedies that have happened over the millennia since. Because it is a day of public mourning people follow the traditional customs of mourning (see Chapter 6). They do not wear leather footwear, do not greet each other and until midday only sit on low chairs or on the ground as a sign of mourning.

There are four other fast days during which eating is forbidden, but only during the hours of daylight. The rules for exemptions on these fast days are rather more lenient, especially for ill patients or pregnant and nursing women.

CHAPTER 6

END OF LIFE ISSUES

The Value of Life

Jews consider all human life to be sacred and all human life is considered to be of equal and infinite value. Concepts of 'the value of life' or even 'the relative value of life' or the (relative) value of one human life over another, are totally alien to the Jewish way of thinking. Because of the belief that all life is of infinite value, it follows that even the smallest part of any life is still of infinite value – because a small part of infinity is still infinity. To Orthodox Jews who really believe that all life is of equal value, the life of a child born with multiple handicaps is no less valuable than that of a venerable sage or a young breadwinner. The elderly, no matter how weak, sick or demented, are afforded great respect both from close family and the wider community and are often cared for lovingly at considerable material and emotional cost.

All individuals have as much right to life as each other. Comments from doctors or nurses which attach value judgements to patients' relative quality of life will be vehemently rejected and contested. Orthodox Jews will go to extreme lengths to preserve and prolong life. Orthodox Jewish families will lavish every level of care on a severely handicapped child or the moribund victim of a stroke, often at great personal or financial cost. This is one area where close liaison between patients, their families, their GPs and local consultants (as well as their rabbinic advisors) is absolutely vital and can be most productive.

Intensive Care

Even when extremely ill and on the intensive or coronary care ward, Orthodox Jewish patients or their relatives or carers may go to considerable lengths to fulfil their religious obligations. For example the kosher food and the *Shabbos* and *Yom-Tov* laws will continue to be observed as much as is possible within the intensive care environment. Male patients will want to continue to put on their *tefillin* daily, even if they need help to do so. A female patient will want to keep her hair covered and even an unconscious patient should be afforded the dignity of having her hair covered at all times. Relatives of Orthodox Jewish patients may wish to stay with them constantly and may arrange a 24 hours a day bedside rota, especially if there is the possibility that the patient may succumb to the illness. At this time, prayer both by the patient, if possible and by relatives and carers as well, may become of extreme importance. Consideration should be given to providing an environment suited to prayer, such as by ensuring that the patient is fully covered (even if only with an hospital gown) and that catheter drainage bags and suchlike are covered over where possible. The invalid or relatives may wish to recite *Tehilim* (Psalms), possibly as part of an around-the-clock bedside vigil.

Terminal Care

Because, as discussed above, all human life is considered to be sacred and of infinite value, many Orthodox Jews will often feel that any life whatever is worth preserving. Staff working on wards caring for the very old, those with terminal illness or the very young with major handicaps, must constantly bear these values in mind when dealing with Orthodox Jewish patients (even though these may not coincide with their own values, nor with accepted hospital policy). Even in situations where life expectancy is short, families may request measures to prolong life for just a little longer (such as the putting up of a fluid drip in a patient who is in a coma, so that he does not die of dehydration).

Any form of 'assisted death' or euthanasia is anathema and utterly abhorrent to Orthodox Jews. Nothing whatsoever may be done to hasten death. Because of the adverse publicity that this issue has engendered, relatives of elderly patients in hospital may be concerned that their loved ones might, in the worst extreme, be actively 'helped to die', or just 'allowed to die' if only by treatment being passively withheld. These fears may not be expressed openly but might be hinted at by those attending the bedside of the elderly or dying and manifested by the patient not being left unattended for even a short time. In some instances, Jewish law makes a distinction between the provision of the basic necessities of life, such as water, food and air (needed to sustain life) and the giving of active heroic treatments (so as to prolong life). There may be situations where Jewish law might see the provision of the latter as being unnecessary, whereas the provision of the former, to which all humans are entitled, is almost always required.

Sensitivity is required when discussing resuscitation plans and policies. Decisions on matters relating to the end of life, such as the turning off of life support equipment, should always involve relatives and carers who will probably want to involve a rabbi in these major decisions.

Death

Where a death is anticipated, it is considered to be a great honour for the departing soul if a quorum of ten Jewish men (a *minyan*) is present at or around the moment of death. Even in hospital, the family may request that a *minyan* be present and where possible every effort should be made to try and help, such as by providing a side room. The *minyan* may well include members of the *Chevra Kadisha* (Burial Society – see later) who try to be in attendance at an anticipated death.

In Jewish law a dead body is regarded with great respect. Jewish law forbids mutilation of the human body, hence post-mortem examinations are not allowed unless a coroner insists on it and relatives may go to great lengths to avoid one being performed. In the rare instances where the coroner insists on a post-mortem examination, the autopsy should be carried out as soon as possible after death so as not to delay the funeral. Pieces of tissue removed for histological examination should be returned for burial if at all possible. In some areas, coroners may be prepared to accept non-invasive alternatives to an autopsy, such as an MRI scan, if this gives sufficient information. This would of course be much more acceptable under Jewish law.

Although organ donation, after death, is theoretically permissible, the criteria for the confirmation of death in Jewish law are such, that by the time they became available, organs would no longer be suitable for use. (Jews may receive organs and bone marrow as well as blood transfusions and may donate blood, bone marrow and live donor organs, such as kidneys, where appropriate).

It is considered a great honour for the departed to be buried as soon as possible after death and a funeral may take place within hours of death. Delaying a funeral for more than a few hours or overnight (other than on a *Shabbos*, when funerals do not take place) is considered to be disrespectful to the departed. Doctors may be under pressure from relatives to issue death certificates soon after a death, so as to enable burial to proceed with minimal delay. This might necessitate the issue of a certificate at unsocial hours; however, a doctor's co-operation might mean a great deal to grieving relatives. In areas with large Orthodox Jewish communities, the Registrar for Deaths may make arrangements to be available on Sundays and Bank Holidays, to ensure that funerals can take place without delay.

According to Jewish tradition, a body should not be left alone, unattended from the time of death until the funeral. Members of the family or volunteers from the *Chevra Kadisha* (Burial Society – see later) will arrange a rota to sit with a body (known as *shemirah* – 'guarding' or 'watching'). Where possible, hospitals and mortuaries should allow someone to be in close proximity to a body at all times, whether by sitting in the same room on a ward, or outside the door of the cold room in the mortuary.

Orthodox Jewish funerals are relatively modest occasions, with basic, unadorned wooden coffins, no flowers and a short, simple service. In most Orthodox traditions, the burial is only attended by men. Cremation is not allowed by Orthodox Jews.

Almost all Orthodox Jews are paid up members of a Burial Society (*Chevra Kadisha*), an organisation made up mainly of volunteers who make all the arrangements for the final rites for the dead and for burial. Sometimes bodies are transported to Israel for burial there, in these cases too the arrangements and details will be handled by the *Chevra Kadisha*. Even when transporting a body to Israel delay is avoided and a body might well be on its way within hours of death.

When an Orthodox Jewish patient dies in hospital when no relatives are present, the body should be touched as little as is possible. Relatives should be informed and they will make arrangements with the Jewish Burial Society (*Chevra Kadisha*) for the handling and removal of the body. Tubes which were in-situ at the time of death should be left in place and only be removed by members of the *Chevra Kadisha* (Burial Society). Where there are no relatives, the ward staff should contact the Burial Society directly, whatever the time of day or night. Where appropriate, details of how to contact the Burial Society should be recorded in the patient's notes.

Amputated limbs should be given to members of the *Chevra Kadisha* (Burial Society) for dignified burial. Similarly, they will arrange to collect stillbirths and the products of miscarriages (where large enough to be identifiable), which according to Jewish law should be buried.

Following the funeral, the departed's immediate family begin a period of mourning called *shiva*, which lasts for a week. During this time, mourners do not go to work, but stay at home, sit on low chairs as a symbol of mourning and receive condolence visits from family and friends. Daily prayer services are held at the *shiva* house. The *shiva* has a comforting effect and greatly helps the grieving process. Following the *shiva*, there is an extended period of mourning during which time the special *kaddish* prayers are recited daily by the children of the deceased in the synagogue and the mourners do not attend joyous communal festivities. Children of the deceased continue this period of mourning for twelve months, but for other relatives it lasts for only thirty days. The anniversary of a death (*yahrzeit*) is similarly marked by the saying of *kaddish* in the synagogue and the lighting of a candle at home which burns for 24 hours. Some have the custom to fast on the day of the anniversary, except if it falls on *Shabbos* or *Yom-Tov*.

CHAPTER 7

HEALTHCARE VALUES

Health

According to Jewish teaching a person's body belongs to God. The human body is regarded as a receptacle for the soul, the *neshoma* and the individual is obliged to care for and look after his/her body. Good health is regarded extremely highly and it is considered to be a religious obligation to seek medical help when illness presents. This is taken quite seriously by the Orthodox Jewish community and they avail themselves freely of medical facilities when unwell. Orthodox Jews regard illness as being the will of God, but nevertheless Judaism obliges them to avail themselves of medical facilities in order to achieve a cure, even at considerable physical and material cost. If, having tried 'everything', a patient is unfortunately not cured, then the outcome is likely to be stoically accepted as being God's will.

Although good health is so highly regarded, it is somewhat paradoxical that Orthodox and Hassidic Jews are not particularly keen sportsmen and as a rule tend to lead rather sedentary lives exercising very little, if at all. Obesity is relatively common and the morbidity from ischaemic heart disease is rather high. Health promotional activities are largely ignored. Similarly, dental health is comparatively neglected by the Hassidic community (but not by other Orthodox Jewish groups) and their dental hygiene is rather poor. Dental caries is rampant especially amongst the children and the need for routine check-ups is largely ignored.

The use of medical facilities is generally based around traditional Orthodox medicine and patients will consult their general medical practitioners, seek hospital referrals and generally make use of all the healthcare facilities that are available. Nevertheless it is not uncommon for patients to consult alternative or complementary practitioners. There may be occasions when following a consultation with a gentile healthcare professional, an Orthodox Jewish patient may consult an Orthodox Jewish professional for a further opinion.

Because Hassidic families do not have televisions or radios in their homes and since most do not read the national press, they may be unaware of national healthcare campaigns such as immunisations drives or health promotion programmes. Important health information or advice such as during epidemics might need to be publicised in the Orthodox Jewish press.

Cervical Screening, Immunisation & Infectious Diseases

The uptake of cervical smear screening amongst Orthodox Jewish women is somewhat poor, possibly a reflection of the very low incidence of cervical carcinoma in this group and possibly also due to the worry that taking a smear may cause some cervical bleeding resulting in *niddah* problems. (See Chapter 4 for more details)

Infant immunisation rates are generally quite high. However there are occasional outbreaks or epidemics of infectious diseases (such as hepatitis A, salmonella or chicken pox) which can spread quite dramatically through the community. This is possibly a reflection of the closeness of the community, with people mixing socially with friends and neighbours, both at home and in the synagogues and in schools. Friends and extended families live in close proximity and families are in and out of each others homes and often share meals prepared in each others' kitchens. In addition, other possible contributory factors are the relatively large family sizes, the cramped housing and the early age at which children start school or play-group.

Attitudes to Illness

Physical Illness

Within the Orthodox Jewish community it is not unusual for serious illness to be kept secret and not mentioned or discussed, even with close family and friends. Patients and their family may be reluctant to use words such as "cancer" and might substitute euphemisms, confounding clear communication. Contrary to current beliefs in the healthcare professions, most Orthodox Jews would not want an elderly relative to be told of a terminal diagnosis. There are some who might go so far as to say that telling a relative could possibly be contrary to Jewish law, where one must "never give up hope". A great deal of tact and patience is required in the management of terminally ill patients and their families.

Hereditary illnesses or chronic diseases are frequently concealed and may not even be disclosed to a healthcare professional who is trying to obtain a medical history (especially if the patient does not see its relevance), unless specifically asked for.

Psychiatric Illness

Psychiatric illness carries a particularly powerful stigma and sufferers and their families might go to considerable lengths to keep it hidden. Denial is particularly powerful, which unfortunately may be to the detriment of the patient, delaying presentation and diagnosis. This can also lead to isolation of patients with mental health problems. It may be hard for patients and their carers to recognise and accept psychological problems, whether as presenting problems in their own right or as components of other conditions. Frequently, patients or their relatives will hide behind a pragmatic medical model of illness, denying a psychiatric or psychological component and may look for a purely 'medical' cure. In addition, many Orthodox Jewish patients who have led quite isolated lifestyles and who may not have mixed socially with non-Jews might find the environment of in-patient psychiatric hospitals very alien and intimidating. These factors can make the management of Orthodox Jewish psychiatric patients particularly challenging for all concerned.

Smoking and Alcohol

With the increasing awareness of the harmful effects of smoking, and with the religious obligation to avoid activities damaging to health, the number of smokers in the Orthodox Jewish community has plummeted. It is exceedingly rare for women to smoke.

Although drinking alcohol is permitted, it is usually consumed in small quantities at times of celebration. Wine is used sacramentally as part of some religious ceremonies, such as *Shabbos* and *Yom-Tov kiddush* services and even then in small amounts. Whenever wine is required for sacramental purposes, non-alcoholic grape juice may be substituted. Once a year, as part of the *Purim* celebrations, some men may become slightly drunk, but this is a once a year exception! Alcoholism is almost unheard of within the Orthodox Jewish community.

Drug Abuse

Although not unheard of, the incidence of drug and substance abuse within the Orthodox Jewish community, is still extremely low. The level of parental and social control both at home and in school is such that teenagers do not have the opportunity to experiment with drugs or like substances.

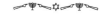

CHAPTER 8

MISCELLANEOUS HEALTH RELATED TOPICS

Care and Support Within the Community

Helping others is regarded as a great *mitzvah* ('divine commandment', or 'good deed') and encompasses the very important concept of *tzedoka* (of being charitable and of helping others) from which no one is exempt. Everyone will do something to help others within the community no matter how little. As a result, there is a good support system operating within the community both on an informal and on an organised basis. All Jews are required to give 10% of their income to charity (*tzedoka*). One of the conditions made by Oliver Cromwell when he permitted Jews to resettle in Britain was that "Jews would not be a drain on the Parish or the State". Thus a well developed support system of welfare and social services has been in place for several centuries. These are comprised of all types of charitable organisations both large and small providing some form of support or care, literally from cradle to grave. With the growth of the Anglo-Jewish community these charitable organisations have become diversified and new ones established.

As the Orthodox and Hassidic communities have grown, a number of care and support organisations specific to their own needs have developed. In the last decade or two, Orthodox support organisations have mushroomed and many new groups have been set up. Most of these are voluntary bodies and encompass a very wide range of activities. There are organisations which provide support for the sick, for the housebound, for the poor, for the mentally ill, for those with physical handicap and for a wide variety of other problems (such as providing help with transport to hospitals, the loan of cots and medical equipment etc. to needy families, or the provision of home helps for the elderly or infirm, to list but a few). There are residential homes for the physically disabled and for mentally disabled adults (separate homes for males and females). In the Stamford Hill area there is a residential home providing accommodation for respite care for physically handicapped children. There is also a Mother and Baby home (called *Beis Brucha*) where mothers can stay for a while following their discharge from the hospital maternity department. There are a number of support groups such as those for psychiatrically ill patients and their carers and for couples with infertility problems. There are several confidential telephone help lines for a wide variety of problems such as those for children's behavioural problems, bereavement and the general stress of life.

There are also a number of 'official' organisations working within the community among which are the Agudas Yisroel Community Services (London and Manchester) who provide a full range of services, including many of those generally provided by the statutory social services. The Agudas Yisroel also run an employment bureau and a housing association providing low cost housing within the location of the community. The Lubavitch movement (London and Manchester) also provides a similar range of services, as do Hackney Jewish Family Services in association with the Norwood-Ravenswood (for children's services) and Jewish Care (adult services) organisations. Obviously there is a need for liaison between these organisations and the statutory bodies and great strides have been made in recent years to achieve this end.

A project of which the Orthodox Jewish community in Hackney is justifiably proud is the Schonfeld Square development. Within the development are a residential home for the elderly, sheltered accommodation, flats for the disabled as well as small and large family units. They are integrated on one site around a quiet square. A small synagogue has been included and there is space for children to play in the pleasantly landscaped grounds. This development exemplifies the communal extension of the family concept which is so central to the Orthodox Jewish way of life, where all ages and generations live together in one community.

Visiting the sick (*Bikur Cholim*) is considered to be a *mitzvah* ('divine commandment', or 'good deed') and families or friends may make arrangements for someone to be at an invalid's bedside possibly even right round the clock. There may be times when there are rather too many visitors present for the patient' own good or for the efficient running of a hospital ward or intensive care unit. This excess and constant attendance of visitors must be understood in the context of friends' and relatives' good intentions and it is not meant to result in nuisance or inconvenience. A judicious word to a relative might ensure a more even distribution of visitors!

Hatzolah

Hatzolah is a first-aid organisation run within the Orthodox community and which has branches in all areas of this country where Jews live.

73

Hatzolah is manned by trained, skilled first-aiders and dedicated switchboard staff, all of whom are volunteers and are available on a 24 hour rota basis. There is a team of doctors available on-call to deal with major emergencies.

Members carry two-way radios and Hatzolah prides itself on the very rapid response time to call outs. The volunteers all carry basic equipment and oxygen and have access to a defibrillator. Hatzolah volunteers are able to deal with most minor injuries themselves and all members receive regular retraining in cardiopulmonary resuscitation. Hatzolah works together and liaises with other local emergency services such as the ambulance service and the local hospital accident and emergency services. Some branches of Hatzolah have their own ambulances.

Circumcision – 'Bris'

A fundamental and very basic principle of Judaism is that all males are circumcised. (There is no female equivalent to the *bris* in Judaism). This is done on the eighth day of life unless the baby is not well enough, when it is delayed until after the baby has recovered. The commonest cause for delay is jaundice, as Jewish law forbids circumcision in the presence of jaundice, even physiological jaundice. The procedure is performed by a *mohel*. In the United Kingdom *mohelim* are licensed by 'The Initiation Society' and are trained to a very high standard, not only in Jewish law but also in surgical techniques and hygiene. Most *mohalim* are rabbis or laymen who have been specially trained; however there are also several medically qualified *mohelim*. Not only does the *mohel* perform the *bris* – the actual circumcision, but he will provide full aftercare and visit the baby on several occasions over the following days. A competent registered *mohel* would always be happy to liaise with other healthcare workers involved with the child's welfare.

Apart from being a surgical procedure, circumcision or *bris* is a religious ceremony. It is customary to have at least ten men present (a *minyan*) at the ceremony and a *bris* is usually performed at home or in the synagogue. There may be occasions when a mother is still in hospital on the eighth day and then every consideration should be given to enable the *bris* to be performed in hospital.

A *bris* is a time of great family celebration. Following the actual *bris* itself, the baby is given his Hebrew name. The ceremony is followed by a festive meal.

Tay-Sachs Disease and Riley-Day Syndrome

Tay-Sachs disease is a serious, genetically inherited condition which is much more common in members of the *Ashkenazi* Orthodox Jewish community (*Ashkenazi* Jews are those of Northern European origin), than in other populations. Tay-Sachs disease leads to progressive degeneration of the nervous system and death in early infancy.

The mode of inheritance is autosomal recessive, which means that both parents must carry the gene for a child to be affected. The gene is carried in about one in twenty five members of the *Ashkenazi* community. Carriers themselves are completely normal, they are perfectly fit and healthy and would not know that they are carriers. Where both parents are carriers there is a one in four chance of a child being affected. There is a one in two chance that a child would also be a carrier and a one in four chance that a child would not carry the gene at all.

A simple blood test to detect whether someone is a carrier is available at hospitals in areas with large Jewish populations. Testing to see if individuals are carriers should be considered for all members of the (*Ashkenazi*) Jewish community well before engagement and marriage plans are made. Testing married couples may be problematic, for if they are both found to be carriers there may be issues relating to future pregnancies, particularly since abortion may not be acceptable. Similarly, although it is possible to test a foetus in early pregnancy, this may also lead to problems surrounding the permissibility of possibly terminating a pregnancy. For these reasons, testing is best carried out on teenagers, before marriage and pregnancy is contemplated. Screening programmes are organised in Jewish schools, colleges and clubs and are particularly directed at teenagers and adolescents.

Riley-Day syndrome (familial dysautonomia) is a disease which primarily affects the autonomic nervous system and which is largely confined to Ashkenazi Jewish families. The mode of inheritance is also autonomic recessive and the carriage rate in the Ashkenazi population in the UK is in the region of 1 in 30. There are a large number of symptoms which vary somewhat between affected children. The following are some of the most obvious ones and which are found to some extent in all affected children. An absence of tears (necessitating the frequent application of lubricants and which can cause corneal abrasions and poor vision); poor temperature control, which can be life threatening; poor blood pressure control; reduced perception of pain; inco-ordination of limbs with an unsteady gait; poor growth and scoliosis. Swallowing difficulties are common and uncontrollable vomiting bouts can lead to nutritional deficiencies. Children may succumb to inhalation pneumonia precipitated by the dysphagia. Intelligence is normal but emotional instability with wide mood swings is common.

Tests to detect carriers are currently being developed and it is envisaged that screening programmes will soon be in place.

GLOSSARY

THE MEANING OF SOME TERMS USED IN THIS BOOKLET

Ashkenazi - (pl. Ashkenazim) Jews of European origin

Bar-mitzvah - male adult aged over 13 years, required to keep the *mitzvos*

Bas-mitzvah - female equivalent of *Bar-mitzvah* but from 12 years

Bekishe - the long black shiny jacket worn by men on *Shabbos, Yom-Tov* and festive occasions

Beth Din - (or *Beis Din*) Rabbinical court

Bikur Cholim - visiting the sick

Brochah - 'blessing', typically recited before eating

Bris - circumcision

Chanukah - 'Festival of Lights' in mid winter

Chatzitzah - substance on skin preventing *mikveh* water coming into direct contact with the body

Cheder - school

Chevra Kadisha - burial society

Chol Hamoed - the middle days of the *Succos* and *Pesach* festivals

Chometz - leavened foods forbidden on *Pesach*

Dayan - (pl. *Dayanim*) lit. 'Judge' a member(s) of a Rabbinical court (*Beth Din*)

Esrog - citron – a lemon like fruit used together with the *lulov* as part of the *Succos* service

Ger - a convert to Judaism

Halocha - Jewish religious law

Hassid - (pl. *hassidim*) Jews of Eastern European origin belonging to the movement founded by Ba'al Shem Tov in the 18th century

Havdolah - ceremonial prayer said over a cup of wine at the end of *Shabbos* and *Yom-Tov*

Hechsher - certificate that product is *Kosher*

Kaddish - prayer recited by the bereaved during the mourning period and on anniversary of a death

Kappel - (syn. *yarmulke*) skullcap worn constantly by men

Kiddush - ceremonial prayer said over a cup of wine on *Shabbos* and *Yom-Tov*

Kollel - institute of advanced Rabbinical and Talmudic studies

Kosher	- (*Kashruth* = appertaining to...) food complying with the Jewish dietary laws
Lulov	- palm branch used in *Succos* service
Matza	- (alt. *matzoh*) unrisen crackers eaten on *Pesach*
Melocha	- any type of activity forbidden on *Shabbos*
Mezuzah	- (encased) parchment scroll fixed to door posts
Mikveh	- ritual bath (house)
Minyan	- prayer quorum of ten men
Mitzvah	- (pl. *mitzvos*) divine commandment ; good deed
Misnagdim	- lit. "the opponents" - *Ashkenazi* Jews who are not *Hassidim* and who do not share all their philosophical views
Mohel	- (pl. *mohelim*) man who performs a *bris* (circumcision)
Neshoma	- the soul
Niddah	- the term used to describe the status of a woman who has had uterine bleeding (e.g. menstruation or labour) until she has been to the *mikveh*
Parev	- 'neutral' foods, i.e. neither meat nor dairy
Payos	- side locks worn by Hassidic men
Pesach	- festival of Passover (in spring)
Purim	- one day joyous festival in early spring
Rabbonim	- plural of rabbi
Reb	- 'Mr'
Rebbe	- spiritual leader of a group of *Hassidim*
Rosh Hashona	- 'New Year', two day (solemn) holyday festival in autumn
Seder	- ceremonial *Pesach* night meal to commemorate and discuss the exodus from Egypt
Sefardi	- (pl. *Sefardim*) Jews of Oriental, Middle Eastern and North African origin (i.e. non-Ashkenazi)
Shabbos	- Sabbath (from Friday evening to Saturday night)
Shavuos	- festival of Pentecost (early summer)
Shema	- declaration of faith said three times a day and contained in *tefillin* and *mezuzos*
Shemirah	- 'guarding' or 'watching' used in several senses e.g. (i) supervision of the manufacture of kosher products or (ii) watching over a corpse.
Shomer	- noun, the person who does the *shemirah*
Shiur	- (pl. *shiurim*) lecture(s) or study session(s)
Shiva	- seven day period of mourning for a close relative

79

Shofar	- ram's horn used during the *Rosh Hashana* service
Shtiebel	- small synagogue ('prayer room')
Shtreimel	- the round fur hats worn by Hassidic men on *Shabbos,* and *Yom-Tov* and on festive occasions
Shul	- synagogue (Yiddish)
Succah	- Tabernacle – a temporary (outdoor) structure where meals are eaten on *Succos*
Succos	- 'Tabernacles', festival in autumn
Talmud	- encyclopaedic work of Jewish law and practice (main source of post biblical rabbinic law contained in 20 or so large tomes, which is studied in depth)
Tallis	- prayer shawl with *tzitzis* on the four corners, worn during the morning service
Tallis Koton	- small *tallis* with *tzitzis* on each corner worn by men at all times under or over their shirts
Tefillin	- 'phylacteries' small black leather boxes containing scriptural passages, worn by men, strapped to the head and arm, during the morning service
Tehillim	- Psalms, often recited (in Hebrew) by invalids or their carers
Tisha B'av	- 'ninth of Av', fast day in late midsummer
Torah	- 'The Law' - The Five Books of Moses (The Pentateuch) also used in the broader sense encompassing all Jewish religious teaching (The Oral & The Written Law)
Treif(a)	- non-kosher food
Tzedoka	- charity, performing charitable acts, helping others
Tzitzis	- tassels on each of the four corners of a *tallis* or *tallis koton*
Yahrzeit	- anniversary of a death, observed by next of kin
Yarmulke	- (syn. *kappel*) skullcap worn constantly by men
Yeshiva	- talmudical college for young men
Yom-Kippur	- 'Day of Atonement', solemn fast day 10 days after *Rosh Hashona*
Yommim Noraim-	literally 'days of awe', the 'high Holydays' consisting of *Rosh Hashana* and *Yom Kippur* and the week in between
Yom-Tov	- festival, holyday

INDEX